If you have ev
you have had to sa
you
then you will be cheered
by the story of how...

Text by Lois Rock
Copyright © 1996 Lion Publishing
Illustrations copyright © 1996 Roger Langton

The author asserts the moral right
to be identified as the author of this work

Published by
Lion Publishing plc
Sandy Lane West, Oxford, England
ISBN 0 7459 3106 5
Albatross Books Pty Ltd
PO Box 320, Sutherland, NSW 2232, Australia
ISBN 0 7324 0966 7

First edition 1996
10 9 8 7 6 5 4 3 2 1 0

A catalogue record for this book is available
from the British Library

Printed and bound in Singapore

**This retelling is based on the stories
of Jesus' life in the Bible.**

Jesus Heals a Little Girl

Retold by Lois Rock
Illustrations by Roger Langton

A LION BOOK

One sad day, a father named Jairus sat and worried. His little girl was dying.

Then he heard exciting news:
Jesus had just arrived by boat
on the lakeshore.

Jesus had made lots of people well.
Perhaps Jesus could help?

The crowd was huge, but Jairus made his way to the front. There, he threw himself down in front of Jesus.

"My little girl is very ill," he said.
"Please come and make her well."

Jesus agreed to go with him. But how slowly they moved!

The crowds pushed close to Jesus on all sides.

And Jesus seemed in no hurry. He even stopped to talk to another sick person on the way.

Jairus was going frantic with worry.

Then a message came from his home.

"It's too late," people said. "Your little girl has died. There's no point bothering Jesus now."

Jesus took no notice. "Don't be afraid," he said to Jairus. "Go on believing I can help."

He chose just three friends—Peter, James and John—to go on with them.

What a sight there was when they reached Jairus' house! People were weeping and wailing.

"There's no need to carry on like this," said Jesus. "The child is not dead. She's only sleeping."

"What a foolish thing to say," said one woman.

"We've seen her. We *know* she's dead," said another.

"Anyone who has come here to get a funeral ready can go," said Jesus. "There isn't going to be a funeral."

Jesus and his three friends went with the mother and the father to the girl's bed. Her body was very, very still.

"Little girl," he said. "I'm telling you to get up."

And the little girl got up: ready for a meal, and ready for life!

A Christian prayer

Dear God,
Sometimes things seem so bad
it's hard to believe you can help.
But you are stronger
than all the things that make us sad.
Help us to trust in you,
to stay close to you,
and wait for you
to make us glad again.
Amen.